D1650734

CARS

This I-Spy book belongs to:

James .T.

AC Cobra
The AC Cobra combined the qualities of one of the best British sports car chassis of the 1960s with the brute power of a big American V8 engine. It could surge to a top speed of 165 mph (265 km/h), and it has the looks to match. There are many kit car immitations so you only score for the real thing.
I-Spy for 30

Alfa Romeo 164
A luxury sports saloon for the 1990s, the 164 has two engine sizes: 3.0 V6 or 2.0 twin spark.
I-Spy for 10

Alfa Romeo Spider
Its classic Italian styling and crisp handling make this 1960s sports car a firm favourite to this day.
I-Spy for 20

Aston Martin Vantage Zagato
From a great stable of luxury performance cars, whose former President first founded a tractor company, this Aston Martin has a massive 5.3 V8 engine giving 432 bhp at 6200 rpm.
I-Spy for 20

Audi Coupé

Based on the Audi 90, when this model first appeared, it was a 2.2, 5-cylinder, 2-door hatchback offering solid luxury and performance. It now has a 2.3 engine fitted with catalytic converter.
I-Spy for 5

Audi 100

With its choice of 2.0, 2.3 turbocharged, 2.3, and 2 turbocharged diesel, five-cylinder engines, the Audi 100 is VAG's luxury saloon.
I-Spy for 5

Audi Quattro

First introduced in 1980, the Quattro sports saloon offered superb handling from its permanent four-wheel drive. The car has been updated for the 1990s with a 20-valve, twin-catalyst engine giving acceleration of 0-60 mph (0-96 km/h) in under six seconds.
I-Spy for 10

Austin Healey 3000 Mk III
This model was produced between 1959 and 1968. Its 148 bhp, 6-cylinder engine gave the car a top speed of 120 mph (193 km/h). This is a much sought-after car by Classic Car collectors.
I-Spy for **30**

Austin Seven 'Ruby' De Luxe
One of the most popular cars of its day, the very reliable 747 cc engine lead to the company's motto, 'Britain's Dependable Car'. It would have cost £125.00 new in 1937!
I-Spy for **30**

Bentley 4.5 Supercharged

Only fifty of this model were built in the 1930s, yet it is the best-known car of the marque. Although it was heavy, the 4.5 supercharged engine could easily push the car to over 100 mph (160 km/h).
I-Spy for 50

Bentley Turbo R

Rolls-Royce Motor Cars, who manufacture this car, claim that it is the world's 'ultimate luxury sporting saloon'. Its turbocharged V8 engine takes it effortlessly to a top speed of 140 mph (225 km/h).
I-Spy for 20

1900 TU

BMW Z1
Powered by the 2.5, six-cylinder engine from the popular BMW 325i, the two-seater, hi-tech roadster was first introduced in 1986 after only three years in development. Unusually, its plastic body panels can be recycled.
I-Spy for **20**

BMW M3
In its first year of production, 1988, only 130 of these fully convertible cars were built, exclusively for the German market. It is based on the BMW 325i Convertible body with a 2.3, 200-bhp engine. Incidentally, BMW stands for *Bayerische Motoren Werk*.
I-Spy for **20**

BMW 750i
The 300-bhp, 5.0 engine whisks this luxury sports saloon from a standing start to 62 mph (100 km/h) in a little over 7 seconds. Its top speed is limited electronically to *only* 155 mph (250 km/h)! The car has an on-board computer which even warns the driver if the tyres are overloaded.
I-Spy for **10**

Caterham Seven
The Caterham Seven was designed by Colin Chapman, the founder of Lotus Cars. It is available in kit form and as a component car needing simple final assembly. Two well-known motoring magazines have described it as '...the ultimate driving machine'.
I-Spy for 20

Chevrolet Corvette
America's only true sports car was introduced in 1953 and is still produced to this day. This 1973 V8 Cid model could produce 330 bhp to take the car from standstill to 60 mph (96 km/h) in only 6.5 seconds.
I-Spy for 20

Citroën 2cv
Like the Beetle and the Morris Minor, the 'Deux Chevaux', as it is sometimes called, has been a cult car since it first appeared in 1948. Prototypes were built in 1939, however, and although the war intervened, development continued.
I-Spy for 5
Double for a 'Dolly' or a 'Charleston'

Citroën 7 cv Traction (Light 15)
This was the world's first mass-produced, front-wheel drive car and was produced continuously from 1934 to 1957. The car was not supported on the traditional metal chassis.
I-Spy for **20**

Citroën AX
Offering more kilometres per litre than almost any other 'super-mini', the AX is every bit a Citroën with its uniquely French design.
I-Spy for **5**

Citroën BX
There are some seventeen models in the BX range from the basic 1.4 TE saloon to the sporting GTi (GT stands for Grand Tourer). Some are fitted with ABS (Advanced Braking System).
I-Spy for **5**
Double for an ABS model.

9

Citroën XM
With a choice of engines, including turbo-diesel, the XM was the world's first production car with a suspension system that adapts to the road surface and the way it is driven.
I-Spy for 10

Daihatsu Sportrak
The Sportrak was designed to be a highly adaptable, fun, four-wheel drive vehicle, equally at home in city street or muddy field track.
I-Spy for 10

Daimler V8 Sports
The glass-fibre bodied SP250 Dart was Daimler's attempt to produce a sports car for the 1960s. With a 2.5 V8 engine, the car performed extremely well with a top speed of 124 mph (200 km/h).
*I-Spy for **25***

Ferrari 348
This mid-engined, 2-door car comes in hard- and soft-top versions and is powered by a 3.4 V8 engine which takes the car from 0-60 mph (0-100 km/h) in under 6 seconds and on to a top speed of 170 mph (275 km/h).
*I-Spy for **20***

Ferrari Mondial
It is just possible to squeeze two children into the back seats of this stylish Italian coupé which also comes in a convertible form. It has the same engine as the 348 and, surprisingly perhaps, at a constant 56 mph (90 km/h) returns almost 30 miles (50 km) to the gallon (4.5 l).
I-Spy for 20

Ferrari F40
The F40 was launched in 1987 to celebrate forty years of Ferrari cars. It is a 2-door, mid-engined, rear-wheel drive car with a twin-turbo, 3.0, V8 engine capable of over 200 mph (322 km/h).
I-Spy for 50

Fiat Panda
There are many versions of this basic little all-purpose car which, in most cases, is best suited to city driving where its economy outweighs its questionable comfort. There is, however, a 4-wheel drive version which, with its raised ground clearance, is a true 'off-road' vehicle.
I-Spy for 5
Double for the 4x4

Fiat Uno
Since it was launched in 1983, the Uno has become Europe's most popular car in its class. There is a variety of engines including 1.0, 1.1, 1.4 (with or without turbo-charging), and 1.7 diesel. The Selecta version has continuously variable automatic transmission.
I-Spy for 5

Fiat Tipo
Similar in its rather eccentric styling to the smaller Uno, the Tipo is a genuine medium-sized family hatchback. There are 1.4, 16, and 1.8 petrol engines as well as 1.7 diesel and 1.9 turbo-diesel in this range of 5-door cars.
I-Spy for 5

Fiat Tempra

The Tempra is essentially a booted edition of the Tipo, and there is an estate version too. The engine sizes are the same as for the Tipo and there is continuously variable automatic transmission available for the 1.6 car.

*I-Spy for **10***

Ford Consul Convertible

The 'three graces' (Consul, Zephyr, and Zodiac) were restyled in 1956. Some were even exported to Australia. The 4-cylinder 1.7 engine was capable of 78 mph (125 km/h).

*I-Spy for **40***

Ford Fiesta

The Ford Fiesta is one of the world's most popular compact cars. In 1990, there were five models and nine different engine types to choose from, including a 1.8 diesel and a 1.6 EFi as well as the RS Turbo available from specialist suppliers.

*I-Spy for **5***

Ford Escort

From the Popular to the stylish Cabriolet and practical estate cars, the Ford Motor Company has developed a family of medium-sized cars to suit the widest range of tastes, needs, and bank balances.

I-Spy for 5

Cosworth 15✓

Ford Sierra/Sapphire

A step up in size from the Escort range, there are more than a dozen models to choose from including the hatchback Sierras and Sierra estates to the classic booted Sapphire saloons. The Ford Motor Company was founded by Henry Ford in 1903 and its 1908 Model 'T' or 'Tin Lizzie' was one of the most famous early cars

I-Spy for 5
Treble for a Cosworth version

Ford Granada/Scorpio

The models in this luxury end of the Ford output, aimed mainly at business executives and families, include rear-wheel drive cars as well as the permanent four-wheel drive versions which give improved traction in poor conditions. There is even a special taxi specification and a stretched limousine version.
I-Spy for 10

Honda CRX

With its 1.6, 4-cylinder, 16-valve, fuel-injected engine, slippery shape, and excellent road-holding, the CRX offers the kind of 'hot hatchback' performance and high specification associated with one of Japan's leading motor manufacturers.
I-Spy for 10

Honda Prelude

The 1988 Honda Prelude was the world's first production car equipped with 4-wheel steering. The car is powered by a 2.0 engine in either a 12-valve carburettor version or a 16-valve fuel-injected form. Honda regards the Prelude as the 'Flagship' of their range.
I-Spy for 5

Honda Civic Shuttle
The Shuttle is designed to be a versatile, practical, and compact yet roomy five-door estate car with power steering and central locking as well as an economical 1.4 engine.
*I-Spy for **5***

Hyundai Sonata
Engineered and styled in Korea, the Hyundai Sonata was intended specifically to compete with cars such as the Ford Granada, Vauxhall Carlton, and Rover 820. There are three engine sizes: 1.8, 2.0, and 2.4.
*I-Spy for **15***

Isuzu Trooper
With a choice of 2.6 petrol or 2.8 turbo-diesel engines, by 1990 there were 15 models in the Trooper parade of 4-wheel drive, off-road vehicles, including a pair of vans.
*I-Spy for **10***

17

Jaguar XK 150

Sir William Lyons began manufacturing sports saloons in 1931. The 125-mph (200-km/h) XK 120 was his first purpose-designed sports car. This XK 150 was a 1960s development.

I-Spy 50 for each of hard and soft tops

Jaguar 'E' Type

This Classic of British motor car engineering is a Grand Tourer rather than a sports car in the strict sense even though, with a top speed of 150 mph (240 km/h), it is faster than most. It is the very long bonnet which characterizes this car.

I-Spy for 25

Jaguar XJ6
Available with either a 3.2 or a 4.0 engine, and with walnut-finished surrounds in the passenger compartment, the XJ6 offers the kind of traditional luxury and smooth performance that have long been associated with Jaguar cars.
I-Spy for 10

Jaguar XJS
In quiet, stylish luxury, this Jaguar XJS Coupé with its 24-valve, 6-cylinder 3.6 engine accelerates from 0-60 mph (96 km/h) in a little over 7 seconds and can achieve a top speed of 143 mph (230 km/h).
I-Spy for 10
Score Double for the Convertible

10
20

Jensen Interceptor

When it was first launched in 1966, the Interceptor was nicknamed 'the business man's express'. This hand-made British sports car continues to combine comfort with performance.
*I-Spy for **20***

Jowett Javelin

When the Yorkshire firm of Jowett produced the Javelin, it was a small family saloon, yet of extremely advanced design. Its maximum speed was 80 mph (129 km/h) from the 1.5 flat 4-cylinder engine.
*I-Spy for **50***

Lada Riva

Based on the Fiat 124 and built in Russia, the 1.6 Lada Riva offers value-for-money family motoring although, by the standards of the 1990s, it is not a fuel-efficient car in its class.
*I-Spy for **10***

Lamborghini Diablo

The 5.7, 12 cylinder engine powers this Italian two-seater coupé from a standing start to 60 mph (100 km/h) in an amazing 4.1 seconds and will then take the car to a top speed of more than 200 mph (325 km/h).
I-Spy for 30

Lancia Y10

This is the smallest car in the Lancia range and its styling is, by today's European standards, somewhat eccentric. The car comes with a choice of 1.0, 1.1, and 1.3 engines. There is an automatic version as well as the standard 5-speed manual gearbox and 4-wheel drive is also available.
I-Spy for 10

Lancia Dedra

This booted saloon car is the replacement for the Prisma and comes with a choice of 1.6, 1.8, and 2.0 fuel injected as well as a 1.9 turbo-diesel. Interestingly, in Italian, the word *Dedra* means 'having lots of space', which clearly indicates that Lancia are aiming at the executive family market.
I-Spy for **10**

Land Rover Discovery

Designed to compete directly with the Japanese off-road vehicles, the Discovery offers a choice of 3.5 petrol-injected engine or 2.5 turbocharged diesel engine.
I-Spy for **10**

Range Rover

After twenty years of success and development, the Range Rover of the 1990s is a permanent four-wheel drive, luxury estate vehicle which is equally at home in town or country.
I-Spy for **10**

Lotus Esprit

When it was launched in 1989, the Esprit Turbo SE was the fastest accelerating production car in the world: its 0-60 mph (96 km/h) time is 4.7 seconds.
I-Spy for **20**

Seen new style as well ✓

Lotus Excel

The Excel is a four-seater, high-performance motor car combining superb road-holding with a comfortable ride. Its 2.2 engine develops 180 bhp and gives a top speed of 135 mph (217 km/h). ✓
I-Spy for **20**

23

Lotus Elan
The first Lotus Elan was launched in 1962. In 1989 this latest sleek Elan was unveiled. It is powered by a 1.6 Isuzu-Lotus engine in either a fuel-injected or a turbo-charged form. The turbo version gives 0-60 mph (96 km/h) in under 7 seconds.
I-Spy for 20

Marcos
With its essentially 1960s styling and choice of either fuel-injected 3.9 Rover engine or 2.0 Ford engine, the hand-built Marcos has been described as a 'truly individual sports car', and offers 0-60 mph (96 km/h) in 5.4 seconds.
I-Spy for 25

Maserati 222 SE

The Maserati brothers were building racing and sports cars from the early 1920s. The air-conditioned, leather and suede interior with its briarwood dashboard and steering wheel provides four-seater luxury in a car with sports car performance — 0-60 mph (96 km/h) in under 6 seconds from its twin turbo engine.
I-Spy for 25

Mazda 323

Available with 1.3, 1.6, and 1.8 fuel-injected engines, this stylish Japanese hatchback also comes in an estate version and a 4-wheel drive model which is not available in Britain.
I-Spy for 5

Mazda 626

The 626 comes in saloon, hatchback, coupé, and estate versions with engines from 1.8 to 2.2 so that it is a versatile range of cars combining luxury with economy.
I-Spy for 10

25

Mazda RX-7

The twin rotor Wankel engine of the RX-7 in its turbo-charged form powers this sports car to a top speed of 150 mph. It is available in coupé and cabriolet versions.

*I-Spy for **15***

Mercedes-Benz 190

The 190 is the 'small car' in this range of superbly engineered cars. When it was first introduced in 1983, there were complaints that the car was underpowered and cramped in the back seats. The versions now on offer overcome these difficulties.

*I-Spy for **5***

Mercedes-Benz 300

This six-car range includes a very expensive but class-leading estate car as well as saloon and coupé versions. They are now powered by the same 3.0 engine used in the new SL Sports car.

*I-Spy for **10***

Mercedes-Benz 500 SL
The 5.0 V8 engine drives this luxury convertible effortlessly from 0-60 mph (96 km/h) in just 6.5 seconds and keeps going to a top speed of 155 mph where conditions allow. Its computer-controlled anti-roll bar comes up in a fraction of a second if the car tilts too far.
I-Spy for 20

Messerschmitt
This is the rare 4-wheel, 'Tiger' version of the German-built 3-wheeler which could reach 67 mph (108 km/h) on its 191 cc, 2-stroke engine. It was a 2-seater, one directly behind the other. The car was only 4 feet (1.2 m) wide and 9 feet 4 inches (2.8 m) long.
I-Spy for 50

MGB Roadster

Morris Garages began developing sports cars in 1924. Introduced in 1962, by the 1970s, when this one was built, the MGB had a 1.8 engine and twin SU carburettors to give a top speed of 103 mph (166 km/h).
I-Spy for 25

MG TF (1955)

Powered by a 1.5 engine, the MG T series made sports-car motoring affordable for the everyday motorist. Costing £780.00 when new, only 9600 examples were built at the Abingdon Factory in Oxfordshire (then Berkshire).
I-Spy for 30

Mitsubishi Galant

The Galant range offers either a 4-door saloon or 5-door coupé body powered by a choice of engines from the 1.8 carburet-tor unit to the 2.0 16 valve version. There is also a 4-wheel drive, 4-wheel steer saloon.
I-Spy for 5

Mitsubishi Colt

The three-door Colt hatchback may be fitted with 1.3, 1.5, or the high-performance 1.8 16 valve engine. The 4-door saloon or 5-door hatchback versions of this car are sold under the name of Lancer.
I-Spy for 5

Mitsubishi Space Wagon

The Space Wagon was designed to offer the comfort of a saloon, the load-carrying ability of a delivery van, and the passenger space of a mini-bus with seats for up to seven people.
I-Spy for 5

Mitsubishi Shogun

Mitsubishi claim that the 4-wheel drive Shogun is a 'true multi-purpose vehicle'. It comes in 3- and 5-door versions with a choice of engines from 2.6 petrol to 2.5 turbo-diesel and 3.0 V6.
I-Spy for 5

Morgan Plus 8

Produced without a break since 1969 by this family-owned company, the Plus 8 combines traditional British sports car styling and individuality with blistering performance from its 3.9 V8 Rover engine. Its body frame is made from ash hardwood.
I-Spy for 20

Morris Minor Station Wagon

When Morris first asked Alec Issigonis to design a new small saloon, he christened it the Mosquito; when it got into production in 1948, it was known as the Minor. Many versions were produced including this 1966 wooden-frame 'Traveller'.
I-Spy for 25

Nissan Micra

This Japanese 'super-mini' comes with a choice of 1.0 and 1.2 engines and 3 or 5 doors. In Japan, the 1.0 version can be equipped with turbo-charger and super-charger to increase the power to 110 bhp.
I-Spy for 5

Seen New style as well

Nissan Sunny

The Sunny offers 1.5, 1.6, and 1.8 petrol engines as well as a 1.7 diesel. In Europe, the coupé body is fitted with the same 2.0 engine that is used in the Primera.
I-Spy for 5

Nissan Primera

In this, the replacement for the dated Bluebird, there is a 4-door saloon as well as a 5-door hatchback and and estate car which is likely to be built in Japan only.
I-Spy for 10

Panther Solo

The 4-wheel drive, 2.0 turbo-charged, mid-engined Solo is built in a similar way to a Formula 1 racing car. And it has performance to match with a top speed of more than 150 mph (240 km/h).
I-Spy for 40

G846 WEV

31

Peugeot 205

The hatchback 205 comes in a wide range of versions from diesel van to sporty cabriolet and GTi models. Its style and practical nature have led it to be named the 'car of the decade'.
I-Spy for 5

Peugeot 309

This is a medium-sized family hatchback in either 3- or 5-door versions with a choice of engines. The 5-door diesel Style model offers excellent fuel economy and low running and maintenance costs.
I-Spy for 5

Peugeot 405

The Peugeot 405 was voted European Car of the Year in 1988. It is a spacious family saloon and the turbo-diesel version, for example, combines fuel economy with a lively performance.
I-Spy for 5

Peugeot 605
This car is aimed at the executive end of the market. There are seven models in the range with the turbo-diesel version offering remarkable fuel economy for a big car — more than 1000 miles (1600 km) on one tank of fuel!
I-Spy for 10

Porsche 911
The classically styled Porsche 911 Turbo contains a 3.3, 6-cylinder, turbo-charged engine which develops 320 bhp and offers acceleration of 0-62 mph (100 km/h) in 5 seconds. Incidentally, Dr Porsche designed the original 1930s Volkswagen on which the Beetle was based.
I-Spy for 20

Porsche 944
Only a little slower than its stable mate, the 2.5 944 Turbo has a top speed of 162 mph (260 km/h) and 0-62 mph (100 km/h) performance of just under 6 seconds.
I-Spy for 15

Porsche 928
This is the flagship of the Porsche range of high-performance sports cars. Its 5 engine develops 330 bhp and reaches a top speed of more than 170 mph (275 km/h).
I-Spy for **25**

Proton
There are ten models in the Proton range which are built in Malaysia in a joint arrangement with Mitsubishi Motors of Japan. There is a choice of either 1.3 or 1.5 engines and 4- and 5-door versions.
I-Spy for **10**

Reliant Scimitar SST
With its 1.8 Nissan engine, the more powerful of the two Scimitar models, the Ti, is a true sports car with a 0-60 mph (96 km/h) time of just over 7 seconds and a top speed of almost 130 mph.
I-Spy for **20**

Renault 5
There are sixteen models in the Renault 5 range from the basic three-door 1.1 Campus to the GT Turbo. Around town, even the petrol-engined 1.1 car returns almost 50 miles (80 km) per gallon (4.5 l).
I-Spy for 5

Renault 19
In this range of medium-sized cars, there are three petrol engines, one diesel engine, and three levels of equipment available to give eight different versions.
I-Spy for 5

Renault 25
Among the seven different models of Renault 25s, the TXE is a 2.0, 120 bhp car fuel injected car with a choice of 5-speed manual or 4-speed automatic gearboxes.
I-Spy for 5

Renault GTA
In its turbo-charged form, the 2.5 V6 engine of the sleek-looking GTA powers the car to a top speed of 155 mph (250 km/h) and the 0-60 mph (96 km/h) time is a mere 5.8 seconds.
I-Spy for 20

Renault Espace
Even though it is no longer than an average saloon car, the Espace can be adapted to carry up to seven passenger or to give an enormous load area. There is also a 4-wheel drive version.
I-Spy for 5

Rolls Royce Silver Shadow
It took a massive 6.2, 8-cylinder engine to ease this 2-ton, 17-foot (5.2-m) long car smoothly and effortlessly to a top speed of just 110 mph (177 km/h). In its day, it was claimed to be 'the best car in the world'.
I-Spy for 50

Rover Metro (Rover 100)

A little longer than the first generation of Metros, the Rover comes in 3- or 5-door versions with either a 1.1 or 1.4 'K' series engine, both with 5-speed gearboxes. The 1.1 car offers fuel economy of almost 50 miles (80 km) to the gallon (4.5 l).
I-Spy for 5

Rover Maestro

The Maestro was launched in 1983 but, for its size and age, it is a roomy and comfortable car with a choice of engines including a turbocharged version with 0-60 mph (96 km/h) performance of 6.7 seconds.
I-Spy for 5

Rover 200

The 200 series of hatchback cars is available in 3- and 5-door versions with either a Rover-built 1.4 engine or 1.6 Honda engine The Gti model has a twin-cam 16-valve unit. The Rover 400 is a booted version of the 200.
I-Spy for 5

Rover 800
The 800 series, designed to appeal to the executive market, includes cars with 2.0, 2.5, or 2.7 engines and a range of specifications. There is also the 825D sharing the turbo-diesel engine with the Alfa Romeo 164 diesel.
I-Spy for 5

SAAB 900
The 900 series, based on the even older SAAB 99s, first appeared in 1978. There are 2-, 3-, 4-, and 5-door versions, a cabriolet, and a choice between turbo-charged or fuel-injected models, each with sixteen valves.
I-Spy for 5

SAAB 9000
The top of the range 9000 has a 200 bhp, 2.3, turbo-charged engine. Like earlier SAABs, the 9000s are very safety conscious with a device to control wheel spin, in addition to anti-lock brakes.
I-Spy for 5

Seat Ibiza

From the Volkswagen Group, with a body designed by Guigiaro, a Porsche-designed engine, and built in Spain, there are eighteen models in the Ibiza range from the 3-door 900 special to the 5-door 1.7 diesel.
I-Spy for 5

Skoda Favorit

The Czechoslovakian Skoda company replaced its rear-engined cars with the front-engined front-wheel drive hatchback. There are 1.1 or 1.3 engines to choose from and, by the standards of the day, the Favorit is certainly value for money.
I-Spy for 5

Subaru Justy

The Justy was the first 'on-demand' four-wheel drive car to offer continuously variable automatic transmission alongside the 3-cylinder, 1.2 engine. There are 3- and 5-door hatch-backs as well as a van.
I-Spy for 10

Subaru Legacy

With a choice of 1.8 and 2.2 flat four engines, the 4-wheel drive Legacy range includes estates and saloons designed to compete directly with the European compact executive cars.
I-Spy for 5

Suzuki Samurai

The 1.3, 63 bhp engine in this rugged little off-road vehicle is linked to a transmission which offers 10 forward gears as well as selectable 4-wheel drive.
I-Spy for 10

Suzuki Swift

There are three cars in the Swift range: the 1.6 GLX 4-wheel drive saloon, and the 1.3 GTi and GLX 'hot hatches'. The Gti has a top speed of 114 mph (183 km/h) and reaches 60 mph (96 km/h) in under 9 seconds.
I-Spy for 5

Suzuki Vitara
The Vitara is a versatile, selectable 4-wheel drive vehicle with a 1.6 engine which delivers 74 bhp. There is a 5-speed manual gearbox or the 3-speed automatic transmission.
I-Spy for 10

Toyota Corolla
The Japanese company claims that the Corolla is 'undisputedly the world's favourite car'. There are seven models in the range including a 3-door hatchback which is capable of returning more than 50 miles (80 km) to the gallon (4.5).
I-Spy for 5

Toyota MR2
The MR2 is a two-seater, mid-engined sports car which, in its GT version, speeds from 0-60 mph (96 km/h) in under 8 seconds. The T-Bar version has removable glass roof panels as well as leather interior.
I-Spy for 15

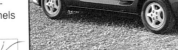

Toyota Celica

In its GT-Four version, the Celica's turbocharged 16-valve, 2.0 engine develops more than 200 bhp to take the car to 60 mph (96 km/h) in under 7 seconds and to climb to a maximum speed of 143 mph (230 km/h).
I-Spy for 10

Triumph Mayflower

Aimed at the United States market, the razor-edge styling of the Mayflower received a mixed reaction upon its introduction in 1950. Mechanically, the car was based on Standard running gear.
I-Spy for 50

Triumph TR3A (1959)

Initially produced for the American market, the TR3A did well in competition, notably in the Coupe des Alpes, Monte Carlo, and Tulip Rally. Its engine size was 1991 cc.
I-Spy for 30

TVR 400/450

Another Classic sports car from a small British specialist company, the TVR 400 comes with a choice of Rover 4.0 or 4.5 engines. Even the smaller-engined version can achieve a top speed of 150 mph (240 km/h).
I-Spy for 20

Vauxhall Cresta

Already well established as a family car, the General Motors designed Cresta cost £967.00 in 1957. The 2.2, 6-cylinder engine gave a top speed of 85 mph (137 km/h).
I-Spy for 50

Vauxhall Nova

The Nova is Vauxhall's smallest car. There are eleven hatchback versions and five saloons. Interestingly, in the early part of this century, Vauxhall was one of the pioneers of smaller but more efficient engines.
I-Spy for 5

Vauxhall Astra

The Astra and Astra Belmont range of hatchbacks, saloons, estates, and convertibles now includes a remarkable 48 different models. The cabriolet version is a full 4-seater offering all the pleasures of opentop motoring for the whole family.
I-Spy for 5

Vauxhall Cavalier

Aimed directly at the fleet car market to compete with such cars as the Ford Sierra, the Cavalier range of hatchbacks, saloons, and estate cars combines performance and good handling with value.
I-Spy for 5

Vauxhall Carlton

There are 23 cars in the Carlton range. Apart from the Senator, the Carlton is Vauxhall's biggest model. The 3.6 24 valve Lotus version, with its twin turbochargers has a top speed of well over 160 mph
(260 km/h).
I-Spy for 5

Volkswagen Beetle

The first Beetle (Volkswagen means 'people's car') appeared in 1935 and production continued in Europe until 1985. The car continues to be manufactured in Mexico, and some of these cars are brought back to Britain and Europe by enthusiasts. There are thought to be 8 000 000 Beetles still on the road and more of them were made than any other car in the history of motoring.

I-Spy for **15**

Volkswagen Polo

The Polo is the small car of the VW range and comes in hatch-back, coupé, or saloon body versions. Right-hand drive cars now have servo-assisting on the brakes which is a marked improvement on earlier models.

I-Spy for **5**

Volkswagen Golf

The Golf claims to be Europe's best-selling car and, in Britain alone, there are 16 different hatchback versions as well as 2 convertibles. The supercharged Golf G60 has a top speed of 135 mph (217 km/h) but is only available to order.
I-Spy for 5

Volkswagen Passat

The largest car in VW's range, the Passat comes in estate, hatchback, and saloon versions and most models have 2.0 engines with catalytic converters fitted as standard except on the diesel.
I-Spy for 10

Volvo 440/460

The Volvo 460 is the saloon version of the 440 hatchback. The cars are powered by a 1.7 Renault-built engine in carburettor, fuelinjection, or turbo-charged versions. This car resembles other European cars more than previous Volvos have done.
I-Spy for 5

Volvo 480

The 2-door 480 sports coupé is powered by a 1.7 engine which now comes in a turbo-charged version taking the power up to 120 bhp. With the rear seats folded down, the car offers near estate-car carrying capacity.
I-Spy for **10**

Volvo 760

This is the 'classic' Volvo, huge, eccentric, and very practical for large families. There is a 2.8 V6 engine, a 2.3 turbo-diesel, and now a 2.3 turbo-charged petrol engine and the car comes in saloon or estate versions.
I-Spy for **5**

Yugo Sana

Designed in Italy, this car is a low-priced 5-door hatchback with a 1.4 engine which delivers 70 bhp giving a fuel consumption of a little over 35 mpg (12.5 km/l) at a constant speed of 75 mph (120 km/h).
I-Spy for **5**

INDEX

© I-Spy Limited 1991

ISBN (paperback) 1 85671 005 X
ISBN (hard cover) 1 85671 006 8
Book Club edition CN1979

Michelin Tyre Public Limited Company
Davy House, Lyon Road, Harrow, Middlesex HA1 2DQ

MICHELIN and the Michelin Man are Registered Trademarks of Michelin

Edited and designed by Curtis Garratt Limited, The Old Vicarage, Horton cum Studley, Oxford OX9 1BT

The Publisher gratefully acknowledges the contribution of the motor car manufacturers whose cars are described in this book and who provided the majority of the photographs. Additional photographs by National Motor Museum, Beaulieu, Richard Garratt. Cover photograph: Richard Garratt. Title page photograph: Peugeot Talbot Motor Company Ltd.

Colour reproduction by Norwich Litho Services Limited.

Printed in Spain.